John Smith
SPELLING BOOK

4

CONTINUUM

Continuum
5th Floor, The Tower Building
11 York Road
London SE1 7NX

370 Lexington Avenue
New York
NY10017 - 6503

© Continuum plc 1961, 1986, 1998, 2000

All rights reserved. No part of this publication may be reproduced, stored in a retrieval system, or transmitted, in any form of by any means, electronic, mechanical, photocopying, recording or otherwise, without the written permission of the publishers.

ISBN 0-8264 5353-8

Original edition first published 1961
Revised 1986
This new edition first published 1998

Typeset by Digital Imaging,
        Formby, L37 7AU

Printed and bound in Great Britain by
The Guernsey Press Co. Ltd., Guernsey, Channel Isles

Books in this series:

John Smith Spelling Books series:

Book 0	0-304-70374-5
Book 1	0-304-70375-3
Book 2	0-304-70376-1
Book 3	0-8264-5352-X
Book 4	0-8264-5353-8
Book 5	0-304-70379-6
Book 6	0-304-70380-X
Book 7	0-304-70381-8
Book 8	0-304-70382-6

The Spelling Quiz Books series:

Book 1	0-304-30050-0
Book 2	0-304-30051-9
Book 3	0-304-30052-7

Spelling Quiz Books 1/2/3
Bumper edition:
                0-304-32911-8

For Spellers

1. Number your page 1 to 15.
2. Read the clue; choose the word from the 'frame' which best fits the clue, and write it against the proper number.
3. Where two 'frame' words appear to fit the same clue, careful thought will show you that one of them is better than the other.
4. Only correctly spelt answers will be counted.

For Teachers and Parents

1. These books are designed to give children practice in spelling once or twice a day – when they come in from play, for instance.
2. Using this book only once a day, a child will go through it five times and write 3000 spellings in 'families' in the course of a school year.
3. Each page is a challenge to a child, as a crossword puzzle is to an adult, and should be presented in that light.
4. Correct spelling is all-important. The accurate writing of the answers is the main reason for doing the page; the solving of the clues is of secondary importance.
   An answer which is incorrectly spelt should be marked wrong.
5. If this book is used in the few minutes after play, scarcely any teaching time is taken up, and lessons begin quickly, quietly and purposefully.

Contents

1. A doctor who operates

2. Something unexpected

3. He was quite rude and replied in a — manner

4. A doctor's consulting room

5. To give in

6. One who escapes with his life

7. Your family name

8. A ball was floating on the —

9. The castle was — by a moat

10. A person who draws plans of land

11. A plant whose stalks we eat

12. Words sounding alike are said to —

13. A disease

14. A beautiful shrub

15. An animal

sur

surprise

surface

surgeon

survivor

surgery

surrounded

surly

surname

surveyor

surrender

rh

rhyme

rhubarb

rhododendron

rhinoceros

rheumatism

1. Inside

2. Outside

3. A private teacher

4. The orchestra had a famous —

5. An engine

6. One who carves figures

7. Our relatives in times past

8. Someone who visits

---

9. A place where things are made

10. Eight multiplied by five

11. Huge

12. The repeated part of a song

13. They wore their jeans and —

14. They drive cars

15. Should be taken notice of

or

sculptor

interior

visitor

ancestors

motor

tutor

exterior

conductor

---

enormous

important

factory

forty

chorus

motorists

anoraks

2

1. A bird

2. An animal

3. Storage building for aircraft

4. American money

5. Near Spain stands the Rock of —

6. A pupil

7. A sour liquid

8. To do with the North and South poles

9. A tree

10. Much liked

11. Please play your electric —

12. The power of knowing another's thoughts

13. A tube fitted with lenses for magnifying

14. We ring up people on the —

15. Usually referred to as TV

ar

scholar ✓

guitar

budgerigar ✓

jaguar ✓

hangar ✓

vinegar ✓

poplar

Gibraltar ✓

dollar ✓

popular ✓

polar ✓

tele

telephone

television

telepathy

telescope

3

1. Spread on toast at breakfast

2. Slices of bread with something between

3. A popular Italian food

4. They cooked — , eggs and bacon

5. Fish

6. Peas, beans, cabbages, etc.

7. Often eaten with a cup of tea

8. It makes other foods tasty

9. A brown sweet

10. Wheat, barley, oats, etc.

Food

mackerel

chocolate

biscuits

marmalade

pizza

sausages

sandwiches

cereals

vegetables

sauce

11. Very large

12. Stupid

13. Many in number

14. The opposite of mean

15. Envious

OUS

generous

jealous

ridiculous

tremendous

numerous

1. Went after another person

2. Made flat

3. Replied

4. Journeyed

5. They — a rosette to the winning horse

6. Winning the prize made him very —

7. Did not forget

8. On the beach they — with their new frisbee

9. Killed

10. Hannah — herself a cup of tea

11. Glitters on Christmas trees

12. Used for drying

13. An animal

14. A sweet

15. A glossy coating (on your teeth for example)

ed

poured

murdered

played

answered

fastened

followed

excited

travelled

flattened

remembered

el

enamel

caramel

tinsel

squirrel

towel

1. Became unfriendly

2. An uprising

3. Diamonds, pearls, etc.

4. To bump into

5. Cleverness of mind

6. Always the same distance apart

7. Gave a sign

8. To surround with an army

9. Your sister's or brother's daughter

10. Has tiny holes for straining

11. To have faith

12. Savage

13. To make a hole through

14. Seats in rows

15. I hope she will — her ambition

ll

collide

quarrelled

intelligence

jewellery

parallel

signalled

rebellion

ie

believe

achieve

besiege

pierce

niece

fierce

tiers

sieve

6

ai

portrait

tailboard

plaice

maize

containers

stainless

failure

1. Indian corn

2. These — have plastic lids

3. The opposite of success

4. A picture of someone

5. A fish

6. The lorry's — had fallen off

7. The sink unit has — steel fittings

tt

settee

Matthew

lettuce

transmitting

attempt

jetty

battery

committee

8. The parachutist landed safely at the first —

9. Broadcasting

10. A boy's name

11. A seat for two or more people

12. A group of people

13. Val's calculator needed a new —

14. A salad vegetable

15. A pier

7

1. The — live in France

2. The — " Japan

3. The — " Egypt

4. The — " Norway

5. The — " Australia

6. The — " Portugal

7. The — " Belgium

8. The — " Spain

9. The — " Hungary

10. The — " Holland

11. Do or say over again

12. The prisoner was — from the cell

13. Under

14. To go back when attacked

15. To go from view

Peoples

Australians

Spaniards

Egyptians

Hungarians

Portuguese

Belgians

French

Japanese

Norwegians

Dutch

ea

retreat

disappear

beneath

repeat

released

8

ei

sovereign

ceiling

receipt

vein

receive

foreign

veil

neighbours

neither

deceive

ough

through

enough

drought

thorough

dough

1. They live near to you

2. A blood vessel

3. To mislead on purpose

4. For their honesty they will — a reward

5. Asim collects — stamps

6. A head of state or a gold coin

7. Not one or the other

8. My bedroom — is cracked

9. A paper saying payment has been made

10. This is worn by women to hide the face

11. A long period without rain

12. Bread before baking

13. Sufficient

14. Painstaking

15. A sparrow flew — the window

age

1. The TV showed a horse-drawn —   **wreckage**

2. A wedding   **carriage**

3. A drink   **manager**

4. Pieces of a crashed aircraft   **baggage**

5. One who looks after a bank   **savage**

6. Fiona speaks two foreign —   **sewage**

7. Bravery   **beverage**

8. We lost our — at the airport   **courage**

9. Waste matter carried away by drains   **marriage**

    languages

10. Fierce

cc

11. I have a Building Society —   **accelerate**

12. To take what is offered   **account**

13. His new play was a huge —   **accident**

14. Go faster   **success**

15. The — happened in thick fog   **accept**

10

1. A small hole

2. A bold or dangerous undertaking

3. Grown up

4. Not grown up

5. The house is — against fire

6. Our new — cooker works well

7. Riches

8. To find out length, quantity, etc.

9. Joy

10. A booklet giving information

11. Mountains which erupt

12. Very brave people

13. Repeated sounds

14. Vegetables

15. Fruit

ure

measure

puncture

treasure

adventure

pleasure

brochure

mature

immature

pressure

insured

oes

echoes

tomatoes

potatoes

heroes

volcanoes

Occupations

1. She acts in plays and films
2. Sells fruit
3. A policeman in plain clothes
4. Types letters for a person or firm
5. Sells writing paper, pens, etc.
6. Sells sweets, cakes, etc.
7. Writes articles for papers
8. Understands engines
9. Sells jewels, watches, etc.
10. Takes care of gardens

stationer
confectioner
detective
actress
journalist
jeweller
engineer
fruiterer
gardener
secretary

11. Used for cutting
12. To go up
13. To go down
14. One who studies science
15. Perfume

SC

ascend
scientist
scissors
scent
descend

1. Belonging to the nation

2. Level

3. A large church

4. A few

5. A burial

6. A country in Europe

7. Upright

al

vertical

cathedral

horizontal

national

Portugal

funeral

several

8. A substance used by a chemist

9. The festival of Christ's birth

10. Kirstie sings in the school — now

11. A school subject

12. Draws plans of buildings

13. Worked by machine

14. A part of the body

15. Hurts

ch

architect

chemical

mechanical

Christmas

choir

aches

chemistry

stomach

1. A plant which comes up year after year

2. It sends or receives a radio signal

3. Necessary

4. Not natural

5. Something in memory of a person or event

6. Another word for cloth

7. First letters of your names

8. In the fashion

9. Worth a lot of money

10. Can be trusted to do a job well

11. Funny

12. Right for the purpose

13. The new duvet was warm and —

14. Easily noticed

15. Something that can be carried

ial

artificial

memorial

material

initials

aerial

perennial

essential

able

noticeable

fashionable

valuable

laughable

portable

suitable

reliable

comfortable

14

1. The satellite failed to go into —

2. A tropical flower

3. Usual

4. A child without parents

5. A thing used to make a place more beautiful

6. Where fruit trees grow

7. Provides music at a theatre

8. Proud

9. The business of carrying goods

10. This type of person thinks before taking action

11. One who writes a book

12. Reddish-brown colour

13. A waterproof sheet

14. Have we the — to stop him?

15. A person who manages an auction sale

or

orchid

orchestra

orbit

orphan

ornament

ordinary

orchards

au

tarpaulin

author

haughty

auctioneer

haulage

cautious

auburn

authority

Buildings

1. We do our shopping at the —

2. Plays are produced here

3. A one-storey house

4. For an aeroplane

5. A house for monks

6. You go here for a meal

7. A building for housing books

8. Interesting relics are on show here

9. For producing goods

10. A place of learning which awards degrees

11. New York is famous for these tall buildings

12. A Muslim place of worship

13. A tent

14. A sports ground

15. A slaughterhouse

hangar

mosque

theatre

museum

library

supermarket

marquee

factories

abattoir

skyscrapers

university

bungalow

monastery

stadium

restaurant

16

1. Leaves

2. Those who are not in the armed forces

3. Straightaway

4. A bridge

5. A precious stone

6. The line joining opposite corners of a rectangle

7. The line passing through the centre of a circle

8. Our laws are made by this

9. A country in Asia

10. The face of a watch or clock

11. Made greater

12. Executed on a cross

13. Stately

14. Contented

15. Resisted

ia

diamond

parliament

viaduct

civilians

foliage

dial

India

immediately

diagonal

diameter

fied

dignified

magnified

satisfied

defied

crucified

1. Karen went — in her new tracksuit

2. The diver adjusted his —

3. To say something more exciting than it really is

4. A sledge

5. Suitcases and trunks

6. To put forward an idea

7. A grub

8. A body of men and women

9. To complete one's duties

10. A part of the body

11. A yellow flower

12. He waited — he was feeling better

13. A cut-out shape

14. A pan is a cooking —

15. A seed put in soup

gg

luggage

suggest

maggot

exaggerate

goggles

jogging

toboggan

il

until

tonsil

lentil

council

daffodil

utensil

stencil

fulfil

18

ph

1. An Egyptian king
2. Victory
3. A man's name
4. A small booklet
5. In some maths lessons we draw —
6. One who foretells the future
7. A ghost
8. A small group of words
9. A section of writing
10. Taken with a camera

prophet

graphs

phantom

Pharaoh

triumph

pamphlet

Joseph

photograph

phrase

paragraph

gue

11. Mrs. Brown found the price in the —
12. A table of teams
13. A bad fellow
14. A disease which spreads
15. Unclear

rogue

plague

league

vague

catalogue

At Home

1. A warm bed covering

2. A small table on wheels

3. Cups, saucers, plates

4. Knives, forks, spoons

5. Keeps food cool

6. Stores frozen food

7. Tables, chairs, beds

8. Cleans the clothes

9. Picks up dust

10. Lights most homes

11. For a car

12. They hang at the windows

13. A set of furniture

14. Your socks are in the chest of —

15. Protects children from being burnt

cutlery

furniture

drawers

garage

duvet

refrigerator

freezer

trolley

suite

fire-guard

crockery

curtains

electricity

washing machine

vacuum cleaner

1. This bus seats 32 —

2. Buying and selling

3. Take the — out of the oven in an hour

4. A country

5. Their disco was a great —

6. The story starts in the next —

7. Ask for — to leave early

8. Brushing is — to keep our teeth clean

9. We need a box of paper —

10. Anna wants to be a fashion —

11. I would like to — my appointment, please

12. To turn round

13. Lisa has just read this —

14. Sharp tool for shaping wood

15. Small stones and sand

ss

casserole

success

issue

necessary

Russia

passengers

business

tissues

permission

el

gravel

novel

cancel

chisel

model

swivel

ying

1. It was hard work — both rucksacks
2. Answering
3. The shop is — a plug with the toaster
4. Anxious
5. Hitting a smaller person
6. Putting into the ground
7. Going quickly
8. Are you — that you broke it?
9. The wind was — the washing
10. Making a copy

ying
worrying
carrying
hurrying
copying
denying
drying
burying
replying
bullying
supplying

11. It was — kind of you
12. Very good indeed
13. There was great — at the end of the race
14. To do something well is to — at it
15. Everyone was ready — Dad

exc
except
exceedingly
excel
excellent
excitement

y

1. Here is a — example

2. Amy's riding her pony in the —

3. Used for injections

4. It's a disease of the nervous —

5. A room for exercising

6. Young swans

7. Something unknown

8. Sleeping clothes

9. A feeling of kindness towards someone in trouble

10. He delivered a — of liquid gas

11. They carry overhead cables

12. A short stroke joining two words

13. A snake

14. A wind

15. The study of health

pyjamas

cygnets

gymkhana

cylinder

syringe

gymnasium

typical

mystery

system

sympathy

python

cyclone

pylons

hygiene

hyphen

Science

1. A gas we breathe

2. An aircraft used in rescues

3. It makes electricity

4. A strong beam of light

5. Stores and processes information

6. Launched into space to circle the Earth

7. A word meaning equipment

8. Shows change of weather

9. Heats the water

10. An automatic heat control

11. Lights which make city streets bright at night

12. A terrible weapon of war

13. A drug used in medicine for healing

14. This measures heat

15. Electric trains are now replacing —

apparatus

thermometer

barometer

nuclear bomb

oxygen

neon signs

diesels

dynamo

thermostat

immersion heater

helicopter

laser beam

penicillin

computer

satellites

1. Ugly

2. Funny

3. Gives to others readily

4. Brave

5. Huge

6. Harmful to the body if taken

7. Very wonderful

8. Name not known

9. Full of mischief

10. Very worried

11. The front part of the head

12. From the wrist to the elbow

13. To look into the future

14. The filling station — was full

15. Outstanding

OUS

miraculous

poisonous

anxious

mischievous

hideous

enormous

humorous

courageous

generous

anonymous

fore

foremost

forehead

forecast

forecourt

forearm

25

1. A word meaning what we look like

2. This is a good — to go swimming

3. A youngster who is learning the trade

4. Her — with the dentist is at ten

5. To arrest someone

6. Their car was on the — side of the road

7. An enemy

8. Dreadful

9. A request (often sent when seeking a job)

10. We — all you are doing for us

11. Not sure that all is well

12. Fierce

13. Kind and well-mannered

14. Lovely to eat

15. Cleverly thought out

pp

apprentice

appalling

opponent

appreciate

apprehend

opportunity

appearance

appointment

opposite

application

ious

gracious

ingenious

delicious

suspicious

vicious

ful

merciful	
grateful	
tasteful	
careful	
colourful	
dreadful	
painful	

1. Willing to forgive

2. Awful

3. Hurting

4. In good taste

5. Opposite of careless

6. I am — for your help

7. With plenty of colour

fully

painfully	
beautifully	
awfully	
cheerfully	
faithfully	
truthfully	
carefully	
lawfully	

8. Merrily

9. To reduce accidents motorists must drive —

10. With pain

11. Dreadfully

12. Another word for loyally

13. Honestly

14. Keeping within the law

15. The yacht showed up — against the dark clouds

Tricky Ones

1. Dad has an — shop in the town

2. The video is — for two years

3. A meal out in the open air

4. An illness

5. Regular beats

6. Real, not fake

7. Lines keeping the same distance apart are —

8. An officer in the army

9. A place where the dead are buried

10. A winter sport

colonel

picnic

skiing

parallel

pneumonia

rhythm

genuine

cemetery

antiques

guaranteed

wr

11. A worm — across the path

12. The parcel was well —

13. To pull quickly

14. Anger

15. I'll — the water from this wet cloth

wring

wrath

wrapped

wriggled

wrench

28

1. A word meaning bravery

2. The marchers — their banners

3. 7x2

4. Magnificence and brilliance

5. Politeness

6. The cheering — the team

7. Protected by thick metal

8. To be knighted is a great —

9. My — colour is blue

10. The planes left — trails in the sky

11. A stone supporting-pillar in a church

12. One of our four seasons

13. A word meaning serious

14. To blame

15. A song of praise

our

splendour

vapour

flourished

fourteen

courage

honour

encouraged

favourite

armoured

courtesy

mn

solemn

column

hymn

autumn

condemn

1. The name of a sea

2. Dried grapes

3. An electric — may kill

4. A dog

5. Fun and frolic

6. Keeping moving (as when making gravy)

7. To give in

8. A putting right of something wrong

9. If you annoy a person you — him

10. The — of water rushed down the valley

11. The track made by a plough

12. A looking-glass

13. A cat — when it is happy

14. The car hit the fence at — speed

15. A fish

rr

stirring

current

terrier

purrs

surrender

Mediterranean

currants

irritate

correction

terrific

torrent

merriment

herring

furrow

mirror

nn

1. Bird-watchers with field-glasses were — the cliff

2. Whirling round

3. Sly

4. The teacher was — up our drawings in the corridor

5. We are — to plan next year's holiday

6. Fastened with a pin

7. Arranged

8. The sunbed had made them very —

9. Used a fan

10. Took off the skin

11. Opposite of outer

12. One who runs

13. A tool

14. Opposite of thicker

15. A flag

beginning

spinning

pinning

scanning

cunning

fanned

sun-tanned

skinned

pinned

planned

spanner

thinner

inner

banner

runner

31

Occupations

1. One who paints and papers homes
2. She attends to the needs of plane passengers
3. Takes care of a building
4. Drives a car for someone else
5. One who works with electricity
6. They travel into space
7. A man who serves meals in a café or hotel
8. A woman who serves meals in a café or hotel
9. Supplies goods to small shops
10. Checks the finances of a company
11. Attends to our feet

waiter

accountant

wholesaler

decorator

astronauts

stewardess

electrician

chiropodist

waitress

caretaker

chauffeur

icle

icicle

particle

vehicles

article

12. A very small piece
13. Cars, buses, trucks
14. We read the — in the newspaper
15. A keen frost left an — on the tap

1. Black ice made the road —

2. An article of clothing

3. Not the same

4. Often awarded for good work

5. To bring round to your way of thinking

6. We each had a tasty, hot —

7. Something unknown is a —

8. Under fives may go to — school

9. An army officer

10. Maybe

11. Sight

12. A process in maths

13. Muddle

14. A sum of money received week by week or month by month

15. A special time

er

mystery

perhaps

nursery

different

persuade

certificate

hamburger

slippery

trousers

general

sion

pension

vision

division

confusion

occasion

33

1. We lost the car's — key

2. A test

3. Performed by a surgeon

4. A place where things join

5. A process in maths

6. We visited an — of modern furniture

7. The mayor and councillors

8. They had — a path through the deep snow

9. Faisal — home on the bus

10. A policeman — us to stop

11. The infants had — animals in clay

12. Crossed out or done away with

13. The jars of jam were — clearly

14. Argued angrily

15. The telescope — round to track the satellite

tion

exhibition

operation

corporation

examination

junction

addition

ignition

lled

cancelled

labelled

modelled

signalled

travelled

swivelled

shovelled

quarrelled

34

de

decide
delete
delicious
destroyed
despair
democracy
describe

1. Cross out

2. Lovely to eat

3. To give up hope

4. To make up one's mind

5. The policeman asked us if we could — the robber

6. Government by the people

7. Demolished

ty

ninety
quantity
eighty
safety
quality
novelty
honesty
majority

8. 80

9. The greater number of those present

10. A new idea or thing

11. The amount

12. 90

13. Truthfulness

14. The injured climber was hauled to —

15. It was cheap, but of poor —

Famous Names

1. A queen of England

2. A British prime minister

3. A famous rock

4. A jet airliner which can fly at 1200 mph

5. The land of kangaroos and koala bears

6. A Roman who invaded Britain

7. An English cathedral

8. The first woman to fly alone to Australia

9. She discovered radium

10. Ancient Egyptian tombs

11. A famous naval battle

12. The highest mountain in the world

13. The capital of Scotland

14. Writer of famous fables

15. A German composer

Trafalgar

Edinburgh

Churchill

Everest

Elizabeth

Gibraltar

Australia

Aesop

Pyramids

Caesar

Concorde

Beethoven

Amy Johnson

Marie Curie

Canterbury

pp

1. Sophie — her rival in the last 200 metres

2. Children are — if an outing has to be cancelled

3. A sweet

4. They are — of the local team

5. Vanished from sight

---

6. Cutting with an axe

7. Taking a firm hold

8. Falling

9. The injured bird was — its wings

10. Visiting the shops

---

11. Knocked off a small piece

12. Supported

13. Took small sips

14. Halted

15. Ben is fully — to go hang-gliding

supporters

outstripped

peppermint

disappeared

disappointed

flapping

chopping

gripping

shopping

dropping

stopped

equipped

propped

chipped

sipped

37

1. First month of the year

2. Second month of the year

3. From infant school we go to — school

4. From primary school we go to — school

5. A country in Europe

6. A book of word meanings

7. The gate in the — fence was guarded

8. Not moving

9. Essential

10. A book for recording daily happenings

11. A rock

12. Where the arm joins the body

13. To burn slowly

14. Chickens, ducks, geese, etc.

15. Found growing in damp places

ary

dictionary

primary

stationary

January

February

secondary

Hungary

boundary

necessary

diary

ou

poultry

smoulder

mould

boulder

shoulder

ck

1. His father is a very skilled —

2. We use yellow chalk on the —

3. Tim needs a — for his sponsored walk

4. Aircraft — was scattered far and wide

5. For carrying water

6. A boy's name

7. To laugh mischievously

8. Worn on a chain round the neck

9. A tall flower

10. The national plant of Ireland

11. The gardener was using the stones to make a —

12. The opposite of forward

13. A part of the finger

14. A bus with an upstairs

15. A wild animal like a dog

backward

locket

blackboard

rucksack

shamrock

wreckage

jackal

Patrick

chuckle

bucket

bricklayer

knuckle

rockery

hollyhock

double-decker

Tricky Ones

1. The famous king with the Round Table
2. A means of escape from a plane
3. The church received a — to help their appeal
4. Tired out
5. Bought from a jeweller
6. A line of waiting people
7. They have three stripes on their arms
8. The light-brown cloth worn by the army
9. A sailing boat
10. A girl's name
11. Hair on the upper lip
12. 60 seconds
13. Birthplace of Jesus Christ
14. Chris — play in the concert
15. A boy's name

sergeants

cannot

Michael

cheque

yacht

exhausted

moustache

Arthur

Bethlehem

parachute

Margaret

diamonds

khaki

queue

minute

40

In Town

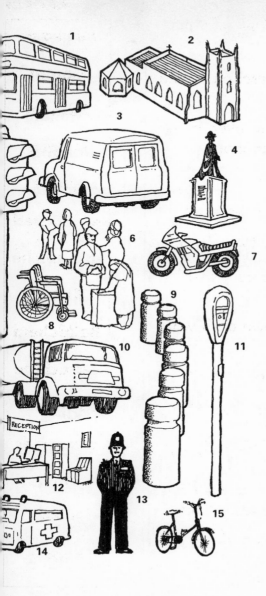

motorbike

lorry

van

traffic-lights

shoppers

office

bicycle

church

bollards

double-decker

wheelchair

constable

ambulance

statue

parking-meter

41

Interests

football

tennis

swimming

climbing

badminton

rugby

boxing

athletics

motor-racing

billiards

skiing

golf

cricket

music

television